The ups & downs of being a WIFE

The ups & downs of being a WIFE

Tony Husband

ARCTURUS

Thanks to Private Eye for very kindly allowing us to use their cartoons.

The cartoons on pages 9, 19, 22, 23, 31, 35, 49, 50, 62, 69, 75, 78, 82, 108, 120 are reproduced by kind permission of *PRIVATE EYE* magazine/Tony Husband – www.private-eye.co.uk

ARCTURUS

This edition published in 2016 by Arcturus Publishing Limited
26/27 Bickels Yard, 151–153 Bermondsey Street,
London SE1 3HA

ISBN: 978-1-78428-381-0
AD005375UK

Printed in China

INTRODUCTION

What it must be like to be a wife I can only imagine. Fairly easy, I would have thought. I mean how could it not be? We blokes don't ask for much. We work hard and when we get home exhausted we're only too willing to help around the house with chores and things. So, yes, life for the wife must be pretty cushy… Hold on, I'm joking. It must be a tough ask putting up with your husband day after day, year after year… very tough indeed!

You might have noticed an unusual phenomenon: when men come home from work, it's their 'time off', but a woman's work is never done. Women often complain that men don't spot all the little touches around the house – the flowers on the kitchen table, the gleaming sink and all the freshly ironed shirts. It's all taken for granted. Do men think the house cleans itself? Well, actually a lot of them do, even if this is slowly – very slowly! – changing.

In fact you have to take your hat off to the wife. She's a jack of all trades and master of most of them. And all she wants in return is a little love, the odd bit of recognition for what she does, plus perhaps a few compliments about her appearance. If those don't work, you could try throwing in a holiday to Bermuda.

Wives are the supreme multi-taskers who organize everything, including husbands, and decide everything (apart from which car to buy of course). How can mere men compete? At least we have our sheds. Hold on, aarggh, she's just filled that full of all that old tat she's chucking out…

Tony Husband

'Charles, go and sort out your sock drawer and be ruthless.'

'I told you to book us a room months ago.'

'Why does the dog always smell of beer
when you come back from a walk?'

'Sorry I snapped before, dear.
It was a touch of pre–minstrel tension.'

'Are you sure my husband's not been in?!!'

'Ow!! There's that stabbing pain in my shoulder again.'

'It's bad news, I'm afraid, Mrs Birch.
I'm having an affair with your husband.'

'I'm very flattered, but when can I get down
from this pedestal you've put me on?'

'Wotz append 2 us Jon?'

'You mean it, darling, you want to marry me?!!!'

'Unbelievable! It's my husband.
"How do I open a tin of beans?..."'

'Oh no, not the George Clooney mask again.'

'... and this must be the little woman!'

'I said when do you get your ears syringed?!'

'I think he's asleep, though it's hard to
tell the difference these days.'

'Just to warn you, don't argue with your wife when she's ironing.'

'Isn't it green bin day?'

'I think I'm allergic to my husband...'

'Your husband's started going to the gym?!!
Darling, never trust a man over 40 with a flat stomach.'

'Come round any time... he's away at work for the week.
Come round any time...'

'Just so you know, darling, you're not my first husband.'

'Harry, turn the damned thing off!!'

'Mother was right: I should have married Roger Makepeace.'

'Your mother's on the phone... see you in a few hours.'

'Don't get your hopes up... her cooking's abysmal.'

'The doctor says I have to lose some weight, so I'm divorcing you.'

'Do we have to go through this every time to decide who brews up?'

'The dog's Afghan, the cat's from Persia
and the husband's from Peckham.'

'Isn't there a game we could both play, Keith?'

'Apparently, they're friends of my husband from the golf club.'

'When are we going to get a car, John?'

'Does your bum look big in that?
Darling, your bum looks big in everything!!'

'So what did you enjoy most: the meal or Anita's cleavage?'

'No, I'm sorry Peter... pouring boiling water on your feet doesn't impress me any more.'

'Scarecrow in the garden? Goodness no, that's my husband.'

'No, Harvey, I'm not tempted. I'm far too old to
take up the trapeze!!'

'Truthfully, John, are you ashamed of me?'

'Could you cut out the bad language?
Or you'll have my husband to deal with!'

'What's happened between us, Larry?'

'Bit of good news about the car: the airbags work...'

'What did Rob get me for my birthday?
A white-water rafting holiday for one!'

'Would you mind talking to my husband? He's boring too.'

'You'll have to excuse my wife. She's a terrible flirt.'

'Don't get me wrong, I really like the conservatory;
I just wish we had a house to go with it.'

'You know, Derek, it's been 25 years
and the earth's never moved once.'

'My wife's trying to give up cigarettes.'

'Police?!!... It's my husband, he's spontaneously combusted.'

'I'll just make dinner before Masterchef starts.'

'Hi, Mum, it's bad news. He's got the all clear.'

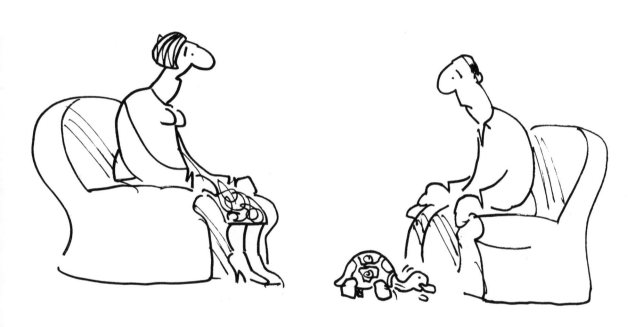

'What are we going to do when he goes into hibernation, George?'

'Oh, ignore him... He's trying to make a point because
I've got the central heating on.'

'Hello, dear. I need to talk to you about your halitosis.'

'When you've done the dishes,
make me a cup of coffee, would you, dear?'

'When are you going to fix the leak?'

'I don't know why you're moaning. I think it's nice when a husband and wife work together.'

PAWNBROKERS

'How much for the ring if I throw in the wife?'

'Hi, I'd like something long and cold like my wife.'

'Blimey, Terry, have you always been a cyclops?'

'What do you mean you forgot it was our anniversary?'

'How does it look to you?' 'Erm... expensive.'

'My husband told me he worshipped the ground I stood on...
Trouble is we were stood on the pitch at Old Trafford.'

'New carpet... shoes off!'

'Frank, the Xpelair's playing up again.'

'Oh, these are lovely, Elaine... Elaine?!!'

'That's a perfect picture, darling, leave it just there!!'

'Well, this just about sums up our marriage.'

'Well, it's a house, isn't it?'

'I'll book my husband in there; he struggles putting his umbrella up.'

'I've a feeling my husband suspects us.'

'This will suit you, dear.'

'I've started putting bromide in his coffee.'

'I thought I'd celebrate the end of the recession.'

'Could you fill in this form covering your
dining and social experience?'

'Robert was saying you play the cello.'

'You know, sometimes, Philip, I think you think more
of those garden gnomes than you do of me!'

'Have you been drinking?'

'Don't just stand there. I've been doing my exercise DVD and I'm stuck!!'

'I'd best hide the drinks if your parents are coming.'

'Joyce, you're not happy, are you?'

'For goodness sake, Tim, sit down... you're worrying Mum and Dad.'

'Darling, just how far out of the way is this
out-of-the-way place you've rented?'

'Then I found this tunnel he dug. It leads to her next door.'

'And don't forget, this is someone else's house,
so lift the toilet seat.'

'Huh! If I asked my husband what his favourite position was he'd
probably say left midfield.'

'Oh, not tonight, dear. I've got a headache.'

'I'm very excited. Robert's got me a birthday present.
I think he said he got it on Amazon.'

'Well, if you'd dealt with the ants when I asked you to...'

'Ha, build an Ark? You?!! I've been asking you to
put me up a shelf for months.'

'Well, according to this survey, nine out of ten women
would have divorced you.'

'How is it you remember the things I forget
yet forget the things I remember?'

'Oh, hi... I'm the wife I expect he's been telling you all about.'

'Mother says... "Stop wittering in the background, you idiot."'

'Er... actually you won't be joining your late husband here.
He was sent down below.'

'You're a coward, Oswald.'

'Do you remember when we'd sit here and talk about the old days?'

'Right... I'm driving then?!!'

'Remember last night when you said you heard a noise outside?'

'I recorded your snoring last night.'

'Happy Times Marriage Bureau, I want a refund.'

'If you ask me, you've turned up the vibration
on your phone far too high.'

'Do we have to have a glaring competition every night?'

'Can you call back? She's watching gymnastics.'

'It will be fine once the swelling goes down, I'm sure, darling.'

'Just sorting the turkey out, dear. Back in a minute.'

'To be honest, things aren't good between me and Dave right now.'

'Bringing your work home is one thing, but not your PA!'

'Curry hot enough, dear?'

'Kettle's just boiled... Oh, I forgot to mention,
watch out for the wasps nest near the shed.'

'Breakfast in bed?!! What have you been up to?'

'Strange how when the cat does something wrong,
it's suddenly "my cat".'

'I said no rude words, Maurice.'

'Oh, stop moaning. Buying in bulk saves us a fortune.'

'I love our Spanish nights, Laurence.'

'You know when you said you'd run out of nesting boxes, what did you use?'

'Turbulence? Oh, I'm used to that. I've been married 25 years.'